This book belongs to

.................................

Copyright © 2021

# make believe ideas ltd

The Wilderness, Berkhamsted, Hertfordshire, HP4 2AZ, UK.

www.makebelieveideas.co.uk

Photographs courtesy of Shutterstock unless noted as follows:
Make Believe Ideas: 8m, 9m (cork board), 8mr, 9tl (paper texture),
20tm, 21tm (bunting).

# Show
## and
## tell

by Rosie Greening

make
believe
ideas

# Get the most from this reader

■■■■■■■■■■■■■■■■■■■■■■

**Before reading:**

● Look at the pictures and discuss them together. Ask questions such as, "What animal is this?"

● Discuss what your child thinks will happen in the book and why. Check after reading to see if this prediction was correct.

● Relate the topic to your child's world. For example, say: "What have you taken for show and tell at school?"

■■■■■■■■■■■■■■■■■■■■■■

**During reading:**

● Prompt your child to sound out unknown words. Draw attention to neglected middle or end sounds.

● If your child makes a mistake, ask if the text makes sense and allow him or her time to correct it before helping.

● Occasionally, ask what might happen next, and then check together as you read on.

- Monitor your child's understanding. Repeated readings can improve fluency and comprehension.

- Keep reading sessions short and enjoyable. Stop if your child becomes tired or frustrated.

■ ■ ■ ■ ■ ■ ■ ■ ■ ■ ■ ■ ■ ■ ■ ■ ■ ■ ■ ■ ■ ■ ■

**After reading:**

- Discuss the book. Encourage your child to form opinions with questions such as, "Did you like the ending? Why or why not?"

- Help your child work through the fun activities at the back of the book. Then ask him or her to reread the story. Praise any improvement.

One day, I wanted to find
an unusual creature for
show and tell at school.
I didn't know what to choose,
so Dad said he would help me decide.

9

I found a camel that was very unusual. It had a big hump on its back and it liked to spit a lot.

"Yuck! I think camels are too big for show and tell," said Dad.

11

I searched for smaller animals and found a chameleon. It seemed perfect, but then it changed colour and we couldn't find it anywhere!

"Chameleons are too good at hiding," said Dad.

13

I hunted for more interesting animals and came across a stink bird. It had beautiful feathers but one big problem.

"Phew! This bird is much too
smelly for school," said Dad.

After that, I collected some ants in a jar.
They were small, easy to see and
smelt fine, but they escaped.
"Oh dear," said Dad.

I was out of ideas.

"Why don't you take a turtle?" suggested Dad.
I thought that was a good idea, but I couldn't find a turtle anywhere.

18

It didn't matter, though. In the end,
I found an even more unusual creature
for show and tell . . .

Show and Tell

# Discussion Questions

**1** Which animal had beautiful feathers?

**2** Why didn't the boy take the ants to school?

**3** How did the dad feel about the camel? How could you tell?

# ৯ Sight Words ৶

Learning sight words helps you read fluently. Practise these sight words from the book. Use them in sentences of your own.

very

would

tell

show

found

take

after

though

23

# ぬ Rhyming Words ぬ

Can you find the rhyming pairs?
Say them aloud.

smell

track

dad

stink

glad

back

spell

blink

spit

jump

bird

split

school

hump

word

stool

25

Read the words, and then
trace them with your finger.

escape

creature

unusual

search

problem

collect

suggest

anywhere

27

# ✧ Root Words ✧

Match each word with
its root word.

Root words:

usual

search

beauty

smell

change

interest

Words:

beautiful

smelly

changed

interesting

unusual

searched

# ❧ Words for Comparing ❧

Follow the lines to match
each word with its comparison
and superlative.

good

small

smaller

big

smelly

better

smellier

best

bigger

smallest

smelliest

biggest